Developing Nu█████████

USING AND APPLYING MATHS

INVESTIGATIONS FOR THE DAILY MATHS LESSON

year

1

Hilary Koll and Steve Mills

A & C BLACK

Mathematical skills and processes

Page	Activity title	Predict	Visualise	Look for pattern	Record	Reason	Make decisions	Estimate	Explain	Be systematic	Co-operate	Compare	Test ideas	Trial and improvement	Ask own questions	Generalise
	Numbers and the number system															
13	Tower blocks	○		●		●		○					○			○
14	Sheep walking	●			○							○	●			
15–16	Football practice: 1 and 2		○	●				○							○	
17	On the first day…			●	●			○		○						
18	Spider down the plughole	○		●		○		○								●
19	Wildlife spotting game	○	○				●				●		○			
20	Maths sports day				●		●	○					○		○	
21	Hickory dickory dock	○	○	●	○	○					●					
22	Dotty shapes	●	●					○					○			
23	Words on a page	○	○				●				●	●	○			
	Calculations															
24–25	Garden centre: 1 and 2			○	●		●	○		○	○				○	
26	Purses				○					●	○	○			○	
27	Hop frog			●	○	○				●				○		○
28	Teddy totals			●	○	○		○				○				●
29	Crazy cats			○	○	○				○						●
30	Daddy long legs		○	●	○		○			●		○		○	○	
31	Number neighbours			●		○		○	○			○	○			●
32	Flying kites	○		●		○						○	○			●
33	Ten green bottles				●		○	○				○				
34	It's not fair!	○		●	○	○				●			○			
35	Roller-coaster rhyme			●	○	○				●		○			○	
	Measures, shape and space															
36	Patchwork quilts		○	○						●		○			●	
37	Counter attack		●	○		○				●		○				○
38	Pack the picnic		●				○					○	●	○		
39	Fly-catcher: 1			●		○		○								○
40	Fly-catcher: 2			●		○		○		●		○	○			
41	Toy stall	○	○		●					●				○	○	
42	Letter sort: 1				●	○		○				●			○	
43	Letter sort: 2				●	●	○	○				●			○	
44	Shape shuffle		●	○				○				●	○		○	
45	Turn around	○	○	●		●		○					○			
46	Mirror letters	●	●					○						●		
47	Footprint fun	○	○				●							●		
48	On the right track		●									○		●		

● Key processes identified on the activity sheet   ○ Additional processes involved in the activity

Contents

sunflowers

Measures, shape and space

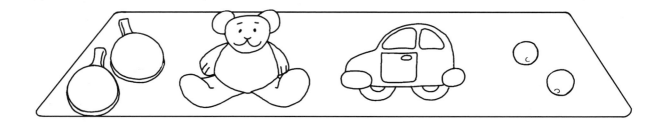

Published 2005 by A & C Black Publishers Limited
37 Soho Square, London W1D 3QZ
www.acblack.com

ISBN-10: 0-7136-7136-X
ISBN-13: 978-0-7136-7136-0

Copyright text © Hilary Koll and Steve Mills, 2005
Copyright illustrations © Sarah Wimperis, 2005
Copyright cover illustration © Charlotte Hard, 2005
Editors: Lynne Williamson and Marie Lister
Designer: Heather Billin

The authors and publishers would like to thank Jane McNeill and Catherine Yemm for their advice in producing this series of books.

A CIP catalogue record for this book is available from the British Library.

Printed and Bound in Great Britain by Cromwell Press, Trowbridge, Wiltshire.

A & C Black uses paper produced with elemental chlorine-free pulp, harvested from managed sustainable forests.

Introduction

Developing Numeracy: Using and Applying Maths is a series of seven photocopiable activity books designed to be used during the daily maths lesson. The books focus on using and applying mathematics, as referred to in the National Numeracy Strategy *Framework for teaching mathematics*. The activities are intended to be used in the time allocated to pupil activities during the main part of the lesson. They are designed to develop and reinforce the skills and processes that are vital to help children use and apply their maths.

Using and applying mathematics

There are several different components which make up the **content** of maths and form the bulk of any maths curriculum:

- **mathematical facts**, for example, a triangle has three sides;
- **mathematical skills**, such as counting;
- **mathematical concepts**, like place value.

For maths teaching to be successful, it is vital that children can *use* this mathematical content beyond their classroom, either in real-life situations or as a basis for further understanding. However, in order to do so, they require extra abilities over and above the mathematical content they have learned. These extra abilities are often referred to as the **processes** of mathematical activity. It is these processes which make mathematical content usable.

As an example, consider this question:
How many triangles are there in this shape?

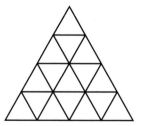

The mathematical content required is only:
- the **fact** that a triangle has three sides;
- the **skill** of counting.

As such, it could be expected that very young children could solve this problem. The fact that they cannot suggests that other abilities are involved. These are the processes, and for this question they include:
- visualising the different-sized triangles;
- being systematic in counting all the triangles of different sizes;
- looking for patterns in the numbers of triangles;
- trial and improvement;
- recording.

Unless children can apply these processes in this situation, then however good their counting skills and knowledge of triangles may be, they will fail.

The 'solving problems' strand of the *Framework for teaching mathematics* emphasises the importance of using and applying mathematics. This series of books is intended to make explicit the skills and processes involved in learning how to put maths knowledge to use.

Using and Applying Maths Year 1 supports the development of the using and applying processes by providing opportunities to introduce and practise them through a series of activities. On the whole these activities are designed for children to work on independently, although due to the young age of the children the teacher may need to read the instructions with the children and ensure that they understand the activity before they begin working on it.

Pre-school children are naturally inquisitive about the world around them. They love to explore and experiment, and to make marks and record things on paper in their own idiosyncratic ways. Unfortunately, once at school the focus is often placed firmly on the maths content alone and children can be led to believe that maths is not a subject of exploration, but rather one of simply learning the 'right way to do things'. As a result, when older children are asked to explore and investigate maths they are often at a loss if their maths teaching to date has not encouraged and built upon their natural instincts.

Year 1 helps children to develop the following processes:
- predicting
- visualising
- looking for pattern
- recording
- reasoning
- making decisions
- estimating
- explaining
- being systematic
- co-operating
- comparing
- testing ideas
- trial and improvement
- asking own questions
- generalising

When using these activities, the focus need not be on the actual mathematical content. Instead, the teacher's demonstrations, discussions and questioning should emphasise the processes the children are using. A summary of the skills and processes covered by each activity is shown on page 2. When appropriate, invite the children to explain their thinking to others. Research has shown that children develop processes most successfully when the teacher encourages them to act as experts rather than novices, allowing them to work autonomously and encouraging a range of approaches to any problem rather than constraining discussion to produce an overall class plan. The children should evaluate their own plans against other plans in the posing, planning and monitoring phases of the lessons.

Extension

Many of the activity sheets end with a challenge (**Now try this!**) which reinforces and extends children's learning, and provides the teacher with an opportunity for assessment. Again, it may be necessary to read the instructions with the children before they begin the activity. For some of the challenges the children will need to record their answers on a separate piece of paper.

Organisation

Very little equipment is needed, but it will be useful to have available: coloured pencils, counters, dice, scissors, glue, coins, number lines and number tracks.

To help teachers select appropriate learning experiences for the children, the activities are grouped into sections within the book. However, the activities are not expected to be used in this order unless stated otherwise. The sheets are intended to support, rather than direct, the teacher's planning.

Some activities can be made easier or more challenging by masking or substituting numbers. You may wish to re-use pages by copying them onto card and laminating them. If you find that the answer boxes are too small for the children's writing, you could enlarge the activity sheet onto A3 paper.

Teachers' notes

Brief notes are provided at the foot of each page giving ideas and suggestions for maximising the effectiveness of the activity sheets. These can be masked before copying.

Solutions and further explanations of the activities can be found on pages 7–12, together with examples of questions that you can ask.

Whole class warm-up activities

The following activities provide some practical ideas which can be used to introduce the main teaching part of the lesson.

Number trails

This activity focuses on predicting missing numbers in a sequence. Draw a trail on the board and fill in several numbers, counting on in ones, twos or fives, for example:

Ask the children to predict the missing numbers and then count on to check.

Similarly, you can start from any small number and count back, for example:

Again, ask the children to predict the missing numbers and then count back to check.

Estimate it

Ask questions such as: *How many steps is it from my table to the door? How many hand spans will fit across your table?* Discuss estimates and then count to check.

Which shape?

For practice in visualising, hide a 3-D shape in a cloth bag. Put your hand into the bag and describe the shape to the children: for example, *This shape has five faces. Four are triangles and one is a square. What do you think it is?* Establish the correct answer by counting the sides, faces and corners of the shape together.

Rainbow clothes

Use this activity to introduce the idea of working systematically. Draw a T-shirt, trousers and a hat on the board. Explain that you can have red, blue, green or yellow clothes and ask the children to suggest what you could draw: for example, a red T-shirt, blue trousers. Using their suggestions, draw each of the 12 possibilities on the board, asking questions like: *How many hats have we drawn? How many yellow clothes have we drawn? Are we missing any?* Extend the activity by including an additional item of clothing, such as a scarf, in each of the four colours.

Notes on the activities

Numbers and the number system

Tower blocks (page 13)

☆ *Processes: look for pattern, reason, predict, generalise, explain, test ideas*

This activity focuses on looking for patterns in the arrangements of even numbers written onto blocks of flats. As a further extension, the children could find the pattern in a tower which has four floors, and eight windows on each floor.

Suggested questions:
- How many floors has this tower block?
- How many windows on each floor?
- What patterns do the even numbers make?
- Can you explain where the even numbers will be? Why do you think that?
- Were you right?

Sheep walking (page 14)

☆ *Processes: predict, test ideas, compare, record*

To give the children experience of how long one minute is, explore how much can be achieved in one minute (for example, how many towers of three cubes can be made). After completing the activity sheet, encourage the children to compare their result with their prediction. In the extension activity, the children find out how others did and collect and record the information on plain paper. Invite each child to show and explain this information. This activity also can stimulate discussion about groups of four: for example, 'How many legs did you draw altogether if you finished 2/5/10 sheep?'

Suggested questions:
- How many sheep do you think you will finish?
- How many did you finish?
- What was the highest number of sheep that were finished in one minute?
- How could we show everyone's results on paper?

Football practice: 1 and 2 (pages 15–16)

☆ *Processes: look for pattern, visualise, make decisions, ask own questions*

This activity could be introduced practically in a PE lesson, by giving each child a number and asking them all to stand in a circle. Child number 1 begins by shouting 'one' and the teacher throws him or her the ball. Child number 2 shouts 'two' and is thrown the ball by child 1, and so on. Encourage the children to stand in different arrangements and orders and to explore the patterns made by the throws. Children can then be asked to stand in row 1 if they are an odd number, and row 2 if they are even, and the exercise repeated. Discuss which patterns are regular and which are random. Encourage the children to explore this idea in different ways and to ask their own 'What if...?' questions to extend the investigation.

Suggested questions:
- What if there were only 10 footballers?
- What if we started at 14 and went backwards?
- What other shapes could we explore?
- Could we use larger numbers?
- Could we use multiples of 10 and count in tens?

On the first day... (page 17)

☆ *Processes: look for pattern, record, explain, make decisions*

This activity helps the children to gain confidence in solving problems using their own method or type of recording. Some children might choose to use apparatus; some might show the friends as pictures or as tallies and then count the total; others might use numbers and standard signs. At the end of the lesson, discuss the different approaches used and draw attention to which method of recording would best show someone else how to work out the answer.

Suggested questions/prompts:
- How many friends came to play on the seventh day?
- How could you work this out?
- What have you drawn? Explain how you worked it out.
- Can you explain to us what you wrote on your sheet?

Spider down the plughole (page 18)

☆ *Processes: look for pattern, generalise, reason, predict, explain*

In this activity the children look for pattern and begin to make generalisations about which start numbers finish on zero when counting back in twos. They will find that all even start numbers finish on zero, whereas odd numbers do not. Encourage the children to reason and explain why they think this might be, discussing it with a partner and as a whole class. They could be encouraged to predict larger start numbers that will finish on zero (such as 38, 40, 100).

Suggested questions:
- What patterns did you notice in the numbers?
- Can you explain why this might be?
- What other start numbers might finish on zero?
- Can you check to see if you are right?

Wildlife spotting game (page 19)

☆ *Processes: estimate, co-operate, predict, visualise, test ideas*

Encourage discussion about what is a good estimate and ensure the children appreciate that they should not actually count the objects but just get a sense of how many there might be.

Suggested questions:
- How many creatures do you think are on this card?
- What makes you think that?
- Are you getting better at guessing now?

Maths sports day (page 20)

☆ *Processes: record, make decisions, compare, estimate, ask own questions*

Split the class appropriately into Red, Blue and Yellow teams or, if you prefer, ask the children to sort the class fairly themselves. Select from the following activities:

Cube race When the teacher says 'go', who will be the first person to make a stick of ten cubes?

The stretch Who has the widest stretch from the tip of their thumb to their little finger?

Square race Who can draw the most squares in one minute? (The children can be asked to judge whether all the shapes drawn actually are squares.)

Dice total Each team rolls a large dice six times and finds the total. Whose total is the largest?

How many? Each player estimates the number of marbles in a jar/cubes in a box/beans on a tray and writes down their estimate. The items are then counted to see who is closest.

Be still A version of 'sleeping lions' – the children sit at tables with their heads on their arms. Who is the last not to move?

For more manageability, several children could be selected from each team to take part in each round, rather than the whole class.

Involve the children in deciding how points will be awarded: for example, 3 points for winning, 2 for second place and 1 for third place. Encourage them to suggest how we could judge who comes first, second and third. The children should individually record the results of each round on the sheet. The appropriate number of horizontal lines could be drawn on the chart before photocopying.

Suggested questions:
- How could we score each round?
- How could we find out which team is in the lead at the moment?

Hickory dickory dock (page 21)

☆ *Processes: co-operate, look for pattern, record, reason, predict, visualise*

This activity can usefully lead on to work on time. To reinforce the link with time, a pencil could be used as an arrow, pointing to the first counter and then counting round to the second counter.

The children could explore the link between counting round from 10 to 2 and counting round from 2 to 10; the total number of jumps is 12 (the number of hours on the clock).

Suggested questions/prompts:
- How many different ways can you make 5 jumps?
- How many hours between 5 o'clock and 9 o'clock?
- Tell me some times that are 4 hours apart.

Dotty shapes (page 22)

☆ *Processes: visualise, predict, estimate, test ideas*

This activity provides practice in the important skill of visualising sets of numbers in smaller groups, rather than needing to count items individually. After the children have completed the activity and compared their predictions with the actual numbers of dots, discuss ways of seeing objects in groups of three or four. Encourage the children to explain which shapes were easy to predict without counting: for example, 'In this shape I saw two patterns of 5s, like on a dice, so I knew there were 10 dots.'

Suggested questions:
- What did you see in your mind when you tried to guess which shapes had 7/8/9 dots in them?
- How many did you get right?
- Could you count the dots by grouping in threes or fours?

Words on a page (page 23)

☆ *Processes: estimate, co-operate, compare, predict, visualise, test ideas*

Encourage discussion about what is a good estimate and ensure the children appreciate that they should not actually count the words, but just get a sense of how many there might be.

Suggested questions:
- How many words do you think are on these pages?
- Are there more or fewer than for this book?
- Are you getting better at guessing now?

Calculations

Garden centre: 1 and 2 (pages 24–25)

☆ *Processes: make decisions, record, explain, ask own questions, co-operate, look for pattern, be systematic*

Encourage discussion about the different costs of the items and the total cost for a packet of seeds and one of the tools. Children may notice different ways of making the same totals: for example, there are five ways of making the total £11, but only one way of making £7. To develop the process of being systematic, the 25 possible additions can be arranged in order, like this:

£1 + £6 = £7

£1 + £7 = £8, £2 + £6 = £8

£1 + £8 = £9, £2 + £7 = £9, £3 + £6 = £9

£1 + £9 = £10, £2 + £8 = £10, £3 + £7 = £10, £4 + £6 = £10

£1 + £10 = £11, £2 + £9 = £11, £3 + £8 = £11, £4 + £7 = £11, £5 + £6 = £11

£2 + £10 = £12, £3 + £9 = £12, £4 + £8 = £12, £5 + £7 = £12

£3 + £10 = £13, £4 + £9 = £13, £5 + £8 = £13

£4 + £10 = £14, £5 + £9 = £14

£5 + £10 = £15

Invite the children to pose their own questions.

Suggested questions:
- What totals have you made?
- Can you find more than one way of making the total £9?
- What other questions could you ask?
- What if the price of each seed packet went up by £1?
- If there are 10 seeds in each packet, how many seeds could you buy for £6?

Purses (page 26)

☆ *Processes: be systematic, ask own questions, compare, reason, co-operate*

This activity focuses on finding different possible totals from five coins. The children should be allowed to explore the possibilities before they begin to structure their findings in their chosen way, when working with a partner. Encourage them to ask their own questions. For differentiation, children could be asked to consider fewer coins in the purse, or to consider a wider range of coins, including 10p and 20p coins. Make a class list of all the totals found and order them to encourage children to look for others and to work systematically, like this:

1p + 1p + 1p + 1p + 1p = 5p
1p + 1p + 1p + 1p + 2p = 6p
1p + 1p + 1p + 2p + 2p = 7p
1p + 1p + 2p + 2p + 2p = 8p
1p + 2p + 2p + 2p + 2p or 1p + 1p + 1p + 1p + 5p = 9p
2p + 2p + 2p + 2p + 2p or 1p + 1p + 1p + 2p + 5p = 10p
1p + 1p + 2p + 2p + 5p = 11p
1p + 2p + 2p + 2p + 5p = 12p
2p + 2p + 2p + 2p + 5p or 1p + 1p + 1p + 5p + 5p = 13p
1p + 1p + 2p + 5p + 5p = 14p
1p + 2p + 2p + 5p + 5p = 15p, etc.

Suggested questions:
- What is the most/least amount of money that could be in the purse using only these coins?
- What if all the coins in the purse were the same?
- Can we find all the ways of making totals between 5p and 12p? Can anyone find a way of making 20p?
- What if the purse had only four coins?
- What if we could have 10p coins too?

Hop frog (page 27)

☆ *Processes: look for pattern, be systematic, record, reason, generalise, trial and improvement*

Encourage the children to take this investigation further: for example, by exploring all the different ways of hopping back a chosen number of hops. They should notice that, on this number line, there are 11 ways of hopping back 1, 10 ways of hopping back 2, 9 ways of hopping back 3, 8 ways of hopping back 4, 7 ways of hopping back 5, 6 ways of hopping back 6, 5 ways of hopping back 7, and so on. These can be recorded and displayed as wall charts or posters and can be a useful contribution to early subtraction work.

Suggested questions:
- What patterns did you notice in the numbers?
- Did you work through in order starting with 12?
- What other questions could you ask?
- What if you could use numbers larger than 12?

Teddy totals (page 28)

☆ *Processes: look for pattern, generalise, record, reason, explain, compare*

Encourage the children to notice the pattern in questions where the units/ones digits have been swapped: for example, 13 + 5 has the same total as 15 + 3. Place value

cards could be used to show how the 'teens' number can be split into ten and ones. In the extension activity, the children make up their own same total questions by swapping the units/ones digits of two numbers.

Suggested questions:
- What do you notice?
- Can you think of any other pairs of numbers with the same total?

Crazy cats (page 29)

☆ *Processes: generalise, look for pattern, reason, record, be systematic*

The main emphasis of this activity is to encourage children to notice patterns and generalise. Here they should begin to realise that the total is the same regardless of the order in which the numbers are added.

There are 24 different orders:

1 + 2 + 3 + 4	1 + 2 + 4 + 3	1 + 3 + 4 + 2	1 + 3 + 2 + 4
1 + 4 + 3 + 2	1 + 4 + 2 + 3	2 + 1 + 3 + 4	2 + 1 + 4 + 3
2 + 3 + 1 + 4	2 + 3 + 4 + 1	2 + 4 + 1 + 3	2 + 4 + 3 + 1
3 + 1 + 2 + 4	3 + 1 + 4 + 2	3 + 2 + 1 + 4	3 + 2 + 4 + 1
3 + 4 + 1 + 2	3 + 4 + 2 + 1	4 + 1 + 2 + 3	4 + 1 + 3 + 2
4 + 2 + 1 + 3	4 + 2 + 3 + 1	4 + 3 + 2 + 1	4 + 3 + 1 + 2

Suggested questions:
- What patterns did you notice in the totals?
- Why do you think that is?

Daddy long legs (page 30)

☆ *Processes: be systematic, look for pattern, compare, visualise, ask own questions, record, make decisions, trial and improvement*

Encourage the children to compare solutions, and collectively write a class list. There are 16 solutions, as follows:

1 + 1 + 1 + 1 + 1, 1 + 1 + 1 + 2, 1 + 1 + 2 + 1, 1 + 2 + 1 + 1,
2 + 1 + 1 + 1,
1 + 1 + 3, 1 + 3 + 1, 3 + 1 + 1,
1 + 4, 4 + 1,
5,
2 + 2 + 1, 2 + 1 + 2, 1 + 2 + 2,
2 + 3, 3 + 2

Suggested questions:
- Do you notice any patterns?
- Could you do the same steps but in a different order?

Number neighbours (page 31)

☆ *Processes: look for pattern, generalise, reason, test ideas, compare, explain, be systematic*

This activity encourages the children to look for patterns in the totals of pairs of consecutive whole numbers and to notice that all the answers are odd. The children should be given opportunities to explain what they notice and to try to suggest reasons for this. An arrangement of dots can be used to help them understand why this is the case. This could be explored at the end of the lesson, for example:

3 + 4 = ⦿ + ⦿

Suggested questions:
- What do you notice about your answers?
- What makes you think that this answer might not be right? Can you check it again?
- Which numbers have you coloured?
- Can you find any number neighbours with the total 18/an even total?
- Why do you think this is? Can you try to explain it?

Flying kites (page 32)

☆ *Processes: generalise, look for pattern, reason, predict, test ideas, compare*

In this activity the children explore pairs of numbers which total 1, 2, 3, 4 and so on, and look for patterns in the number of pairs they find for each total. Begin the lesson by discussing ways of making the total 6 and draw a kite and bows on the board. Discuss that 1 and 5 is the same as 5 and 1 for this activity. The children should discover the following pattern:

kite total	number of bows
1	1
2	2
3	2
4	3
5	3
6	4
7	4

They should use this pattern to make predictions about the number of bows for other kite totals.

Suggested questions:
- What do you notice?
- How can this help us to decide how many bows other kites will have?

Ten green bottles (page 33)

☆ *Processes: record, explain, compare, make decisions*

The focus of this activity is on helping the children to realise the importance of recording their thinking clearly. Whichever way they record their investigations at this stage, the children should be able to use their recordings to recall what they did. Remind them: 'The clearer the recording, the easier it is to remember what you did and the easier it is for someone else to understand your thinking.' Once the children have recorded several different subtractions, ask them to explain their work to a partner. The different ways of recording should be compared as a class, and attention can then be drawn to any use of standard signs, such as '='.

Suggested questions:
- Can you explain to us what this means?
- How did you work these out?
- Do you know what this sign that [Jo] has used means?

It's not fair! (page 34)

☆ *Processes: look for pattern, be systematic, reason, predict, test ideas, record*

This activity encourages the children to look for pattern in their answers and to make predictions about other solutions, before testing their ideas. The children are asked to find all the unfair ways of sharing 8 sweets (4 ways) and 10 sweets (5 ways). They should be encouraged to notice that half of 8 is 4 and half of 10 is 5, and then to use this information to make a prediction about the number of ways for 12 sweets (6). Some children will not discover this relationship, but the experience of looking for patterns in the numbers and of being systematic in finding different ways is an important process.

Suggested questions:
- How many different ways have you found?
- Do you think there are any more ways?
- How many more ways did you find?
- What do you know about 8 and 4? 10 and 5?
- How many ways will there be for 12 sweets?
- How could you check whether you are right?

Roller-coaster rhyme (page 35)

☆ *Processes: record, be systematic, make decisions, compare, reason, ask own questions*

For differentiation, the rhyme and illustration could be altered to show 10 chairs instead of 20. Some children may choose to record their answers pictorially; some may use words and numerals; others may choose to work practically to find the solutions. Allow them to make their own decisions, and reinforce good practice at the end of the lesson. Invite the children to share their methods, in particular those who have tried to work systematically by starting with a large or small number of children and choosing one more or one fewer each time: for example, 1 child, 19 empty seats; 2 children, 18 empty seats, and so on.

Suggested questions:
- What if there were 10 children?
- Do you think there are other numbers you could try?
- Can you explain why you set it out like that?
- If you did this again, which way would you set it out?
- What do you notice about [Meera]'s way of working?

Measures, shape and space

Patchwork quilts (page 36)

☆ *Processes: trial and improvement, be systematic, compare, visualise, look for pattern*

In this activity the children begin the process of working systematically. There are more than 40 different ways of colouring the quilts to meet the given criteria (of which half are rotations of other quilts). Once the children have compared and discussed the different ways they have found, a class list could be compiled. A display can be organised in a structured way to help the children begin to think systematically (for example, start with all the quilts that have a red square at top left, or pair up quilts that are the same when rotated).

Suggested questions:
- How many quilts have you coloured with a red square at top left?
- Are any of your quilts the same?
- Can you think of another way to colour the quilt using a yellow square at top left?

- How did you decide what to colour next?
- Are any touching squares the same colour?
- Can you find a quilt with a blue square at the top left? Which colour is next to it?

Counter attack (page 37)

☆ Processes: *be systematic, visualise, trial and improvement, look for pattern, reason, generalise, compare*

This activity encourages the children to improve upon trial and improvement approaches by being systematic. They should begin to notice that, rather than focusing on the counters, it is more useful to focus on where the empty space is. In this way they will begin to deduce that there are as many different solutions as there are squares in the grid.

Suggested questions/prompts:
- Tell me what you noticed.
- Talk to a partner about what you did.
- What did you learn from these activities?

Pack the picnic (page 38)

☆ Processes: *visualise, test ideas, trial and improvement, make decisions, compare*

The focus of this activity is on visualising, using trial and improvement strategies and developing perseverance. The seven picnic items can be arranged in different ways, but the row of sandwiches always needs to be placed horizontally. Ensure the children realise that the pieces must not overlap. The picnic items can be stuck in place, coloured and displayed so that the children can discuss and compare each other's arrangements, and look for differences between them.

Suggested questions/prompts:
- Can you fit this into the basket? Which way must it go?
- Try moving one of the larger pieces to see if you can make it work.
- Have you got all seven pieces there?
- How is your picnic basket different from [Zoe]'s?
- Which picnic baskets are the same?

Fly-catcher: 1 (page 39)

☆ Processes: *look for pattern, explain, reason, generalise*

This activity asks the children to draw different routes across a 3×3 grid, write each route as a sequence of numbers, and then look for patterns in the totals of the numbers. They should find that all routes total six. Once the children have discovered the pattern, encourage them to use it to check their answers. You could make extra copies of the sheet and draw on routes for the children to explore and describe.

Suggested questions/prompts:
- What do you notice about the numbers in each route? Explain it to your partner.
- What do you notice about all the totals?
- Why do you think this could be?

Fly-catcher: 2 (page 40)

☆ Processes: *look for pattern, be systematic, explain, reason, compare, test ideas*

This activity follows on from the previous one by introducing a 4×3 grid and a 4×4 grid. The children should write different routes from the spider to the fly using the approach introduced in the previous activity. Encourage them to think back to what they discovered in the last activity about the totals of the numbers in each route, and to use this to predict what these routes will total. Ask the children to compare their routes and, as a class, collate a list of routes which can be displayed on the wall. Further fly-catching work could be explored on squared paper, with the children asking 'What if…' questions, such as, 'What if we had a larger or smaller grid?'

Suggested questions:
- How many different routes have you found?
- How could you check that you have given them the correct names?
- What do you notice about the totals?
- Do you think there are other routes that you still haven't found? What makes you think there might be?
- What other ways of making 7 are there? Could we draw routes to match these?

Toy stall (page 41)

☆ Processes: *be systematic, record, predict, visualise, trial and improvement, ask own questions*

This activity requires perseverance in order to find all the combinations. If children begin to lose heart, ask them to compare their solutions with a friend. For a further extension activity, an extra toy could be added, such as a rocket, and the children could explore possible answers if two or three toys were bought.

Suggested questions:
- Have you found all the different ways?
- How could you check?
- How many of your answers include a teddy/bat/car?
- Can you think of a question that starts with 'What if…'?

Letter sort: 1 and 2 (pages 42–43)

☆ Processes: *compare, reason, record, make decisions, explain, ask own questions*

In *Letter sort: 1*, do not prescribe how the children should either sort or record initially; encourage them to make their own decisions and to suggest their own ways of sorting and recording. In *Letter sort: 2*, the children compare features of the letters using ideas of straight and curved lines. This type of classification is important in helping the children to organise their own thoughts in systematic ways. Encourage them to discuss and explain their reasoning and, in particular, to discuss letters that may not be straightforward to classify: for example, 'Is there a straight part to the letters 'y' or 'e'? Does the dot of the letter 'i' count as a curved line?' Ensure the children realise that there are not necessarily 'correct' answers to these questions, and that they should make their own decisions and be able to justify them to others.

Suggested questions/prompts:
- How could you sort these letters?
- Can you explain why you put this letter here?
- How could you record this for others to understand?
- Explain your thinking to your partner.

Shape shuffle (page 44)

☆ *Processes: visualise, compare, make decisions, ask own questions, test ideas, look for pattern*

In this activity the children begin observing features of shapes and explore symmetry and numbers of sides. Allow them time to explore and describe the shapes in their own way and to formulate their own questions to explore: for example, 'Is it possible to make a large triangle? How many rectangles can I make?' Once the children have decided on their shapes, these can be stuck onto large pieces of paper, labelled by the children, coloured and displayed. Ask further questions about the shapes, encouraging the children to compare and describe differences between them. To make a more permanent resource, the cards could be enlarged onto card and laminated.

Suggested questions/prompts:
- What is special about this shape?
- How many sides does this shape have?
- Do you know what a shape with three straight sides is called?
- Tell us about the shapes you have made.

Turn around (page 45)

☆ *Processes: look for pattern, reason, predict, visualise, test ideas, explain*

This activity encourages the children to look for patterns in answers. Here they use a cut-out arrow and dial to explore how many half turns are needed to return the arrow to its starting position, trying out a range of even and odd numbers of half turns. Encourage discussion and, when the children have completed the activity, compose two generalised statements about what they have found: for example, 'An even number of half turns always ends on A. An odd number of half turns always ends on B.' The children can then predict other outcomes and test their ideas practically.

Suggested questions:
- What do you notice?
- Which numbers of half turns end on B?
- Can you think of any other numbers of half turns that might get the arrow back to A?
- Can you explain why you think that might be?
- Can we make a true sentence about what we have found?

Mirror letters (page 46)

☆ *Processes: visualise, predict, test ideas, explain*

This activity provides an opportunity for the children to practise visualising reflections of shapes in mirror lines.

Suggested questions:
- Do you think this will make a real letter?
- Why do you think it will?
- Which letter do you think it will make?
- Can you think of other letters that we could reflect in the same way?

Footprint fun (page 47)

☆ *Processes: estimate, test ideas, visualise, predict*

In this activity the children estimate the length of a footprint (in cubes) and then check using actual cubes. The extension activity asks them to estimate and measure the length of their own shoe. Compare results as a class and compile a list of the lengths of the children's shoes.

Suggested questions:
- Which footprint is largest/smallest?
- How many cubes long do you think this footprint is?
- How could you check?
- What about your own shoe?

On the right track (page 48)

☆ *Processes: visualise, trial and improvement, compare*

This activity requires perseverance. Some children may not yet be able to visualise a continuous track; fitting pieces together is very useful in helping them to develop such skills. Even if children do not find a 'continuous track' solution, their arrangements can be stuck down and used for display and discussion. Children who are finding it difficult can be told to arrange the cards in a 3 × 3 square and to look for:

pieces that might be corner pieces

or the centre piece.

Here are two solutions:

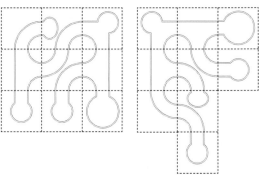

Suggested questions/prompts:
- Tell us about your track.
- Did you find this easy/hard? Why do you think that was?

Tower blocks

Look for patterns and reason

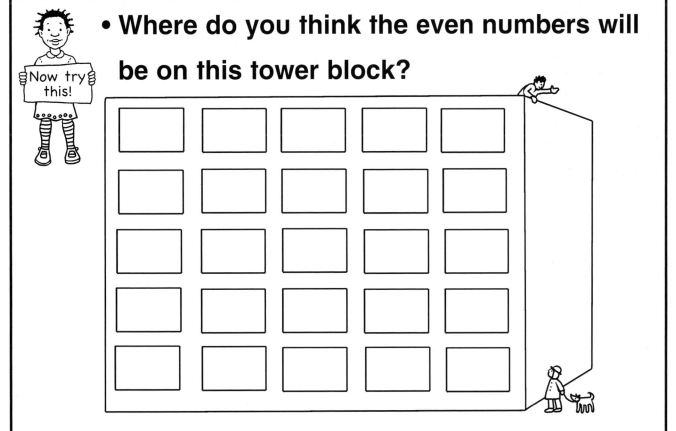

Tower 1

9	10
7	8
5	6
3	4
1	2

Tower 2

13	14	15
10	11	12
7	8	9
4	5	6
1	2	3

Tower 3

17	18	19	20
13	14	15	16
9	10	11	12
5	6	7	8
1	2	3	4

- **Colour all the even numbers.**

- **Talk to a friend about what you notice.**

Now try this!

- **Where do you think the even numbers will be on this tower block?**

- **Fill in the numbers to check.**

Teachers' note Encourage the children to describe what they notice to a partner, and introduce the vocabulary 'straight lines' and 'diagonal patterns'. Ask them to say why they think some tower blocks show one type of pattern and others another, and draw attention to the number of windows on each floor of the block. Provide a list of even numbers on the board if necessary.

**Developing Numeracy
Using & Applying Maths
Year 1
© A & C BLACK**

Sheep walking

Make predictions and test your ideas

- **Use a 1-minute sand timer.**

- **Carefully draw** $\boxed{4}$ **legs on each sheep.**

- **Ring the sheep you think you will reach.**

- **How many sheep did you finish?**

  • **Ask your friends how many sheep they finished.** $\boxed{\text{Record}}$ **what you find out.**

Teachers' note First show the children how to use a one-minute sand timer (or alternatively you could say 'start' and 'stop' after one minute). Ensure the children understand that when the time starts, they are going to draw four legs on each sheep in turn, working along the rows. Then ask them to predict which sheep they think they will reach in one minute. Discuss and compare their predictions. Allow the children to record what they find out in their own way.

**Developing Numeracy
Using & Applying Maths
Year 1
© A & C BLACK**

14

14 footballers stand in 2 lines.

They kick the ball in order.

• Join the numbers in order from 1 **to** 14 **.**

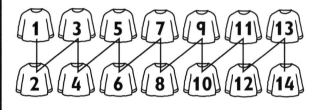

• Write numbers to make a pattern of your own.

• Talk to a friend about your pattern.

Now try this!

The footballers stand in a circle.

• Make your own circle patterns.

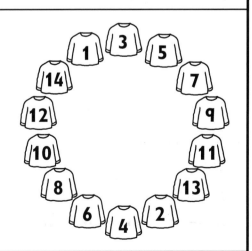

Teachers' note This activity could be introduced practically in a PE lesson (see page 7). For the extension activity, the children can use a copy of page 16. The idea can be extended in many ways. The children could look at other ways of arranging the footballers (for example, in a rectangle as shown on page 16), or they could explore patterns using a different number of footballers. Also try changing the order in which the ball is kicked (for example, starting with the largest number).

**Developing Numeracy
Using & Applying Maths
Year 1
© A & C BLACK**

Look for patterns

• **Make your own football practice patterns.**

Now try this!

• **Now make some rectangle patterns. Use squared paper.**

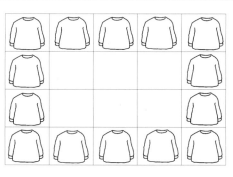

Teachers' note The children should first complete the activity on page 15. This sheet can be enlarged if necessary. Provide squared paper for the extension activity.

Developing Numeracy
Using & Applying Maths
Year 1
© A & C BLACK

On the first day...

On the first day of April
1 friend came to play.
She came to
play with me.

On the second day of April
2 friends came to play.
They came to
play with me.

On the third day of April…

• **How many friends came on the**

third day? ☐

sixth day? ☐

fourth day? ☐

fifth day? ☐

seventh day? ☐

• **How many friends** │altogether│ **came in the first** │7│ **days?** (Record your work here.)

• **Work out how many friends came to play in the first** │10│ **days..**

Teachers' note This rhyme can be said to the same rhythm as verse 1 of 'On the first day of Christmas'. At the start of the lesson, say the rhyme several times from one to seven days, with children acting it out. Ask the children to suggest why we might stop at seven (there are seven days in a week). Encourage the children to make their own decisions about method and recording.

**Developing Numeracy
Using & Applying Maths
Year 1
© A & C BLACK**

Spider down the plughole

Look for patterns and generalise

- **Place a counter on** 26 **.**
- **Jump in 2s towards the plughole.**
- **Tick** ✔ **whether you land on** 0 **.**

yes ☐　no ☐

27　26　25　24

23

22

21

20

8　7

6

9

5

10

1　0

19

4

11

2　3

18

12

17

13

16

14　15

- **Start on these numbers. Do you land on** 0 **?**

24	yes		no		27	yes		no	
23	yes		no		22	yes		no	
25	yes		no		19	yes		no	

Teachers' note Each child will require a counter for this activity. Encourage the children to say the numbers aloud as they jump, to reinforce the patterns. Talk about the patterns they notice and draw attention to the units/ones digit of the start numbers that finish on zero. As an extension, the children could list all the start numbers that finish on zero. They could also explore jumping in threes from different start numbers to see which finish on zero.

**Developing Numeracy
Using & Applying Maths
Year 1**
© A & C BLACK

Wildlife spotting game

• Play this game with a friend.

☆ Cut out the cards. Spread them out face down.

☆ Take turns to pick a card. **Estimate** the number of animals. Then count to **check**.

☆ If you were right, keep the card. If not, put it back.

☆ The winner is the player with the most cards.

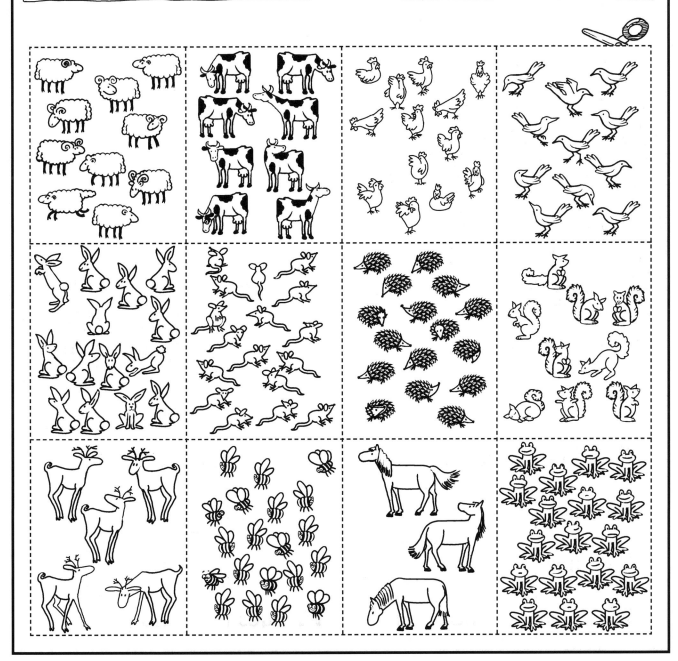

Teachers' note Ensure the children understand that when estimating, they should not actually count the animals. The children could check each other's estimates. Make sure that they do not count by crossing off, because if the estimate is wrong, the card goes back into the game. As an extension activity, the children could make their own version of the game with up to 20 creatures on each card.

**Developing Numeracy
Using & Applying Maths
Year 1
© A & C BLACK**

Maths sports day

- **Have your own maths sports day. Record the scores on this chart.**

Game	Scores		
	Red	Yellow	Blue

- **Which team came**

1st? _____   2nd? _____   3rd? _____

Teachers' note See page 8 for suggestions of classroom activities for a 'maths sports day'. The activities include timed games, races and measurement tasks. The class should be split into Red, Blue and Yellow teams. Involve the children in deciding how points will be awarded: for example, 3 points for winning, 2 for second place and 1 for third place. Stress the importance of recording information clearly, as an aid to memory and for others to use.

**Developing Numeracy
Using & Applying Maths
Year 1
© A & C BLACK**

Hickory dickory dock

Co-operate and look for patterns

• Work with a friend.

☆ Put 2 counters anywhere on the clock.

☆ Start at one counter. Jump round until you reach the other counter.

☆ Record the number of jumps. | $10 \rightarrow 2$ is 4 jumps |

☆ Sort your findings into groups by the number of jumps.

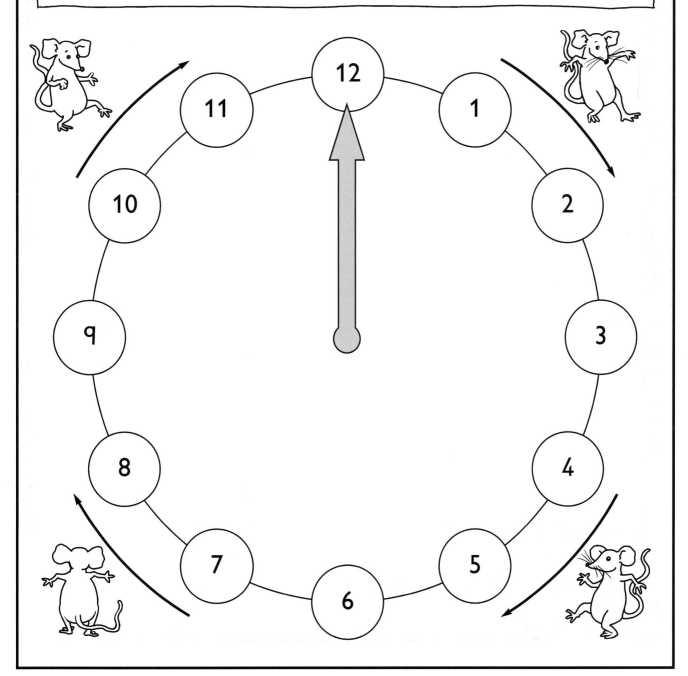

Teachers' note Each pair of children will need a copy of the sheet, two counters and paper for recording. They could record each result on a separate strip of paper, for ease of sorting. Explain that they should always move in a clockwise direction, and stress that it is the jumps they are counting, not the numbers in between. As an extension, the children could find all 12 arrangements of counters where there are four jumps.

Developing Numeracy
Using & Applying Maths
Year 1
© A & C BLACK

Dotty shapes

Visualise and make predictions

- **Tick** ✔ **the shapes that you think have exactly**

  dots. Do _not_ count the dots.

- **Now try this!** • **Now count the dots. Write how many.**

Teachers' note This activity encourages children to see sets of objects and gain a sense of the number of objects without counting each item. Write the number 7, 8 or 9 into the box at the top, according to the abilities of the children. Explain that they must tick the shapes that they *think* have exactly that number of dots. Give the children a limited period of time to do this (for example, 30 seconds), before asking them to check their predictions by counting the dots in each shape.

**Developing Numeracy
Using & Applying Maths
Year 1
© A & C BLACK**

22

Words on a page

Make estimates, compare and co-operate

Your teacher will give you 4 reading books.

- ☆ Work with a friend.
- ☆ Take one book at a time. Find pages 8 and 9.
- ☆ **Estimate** the number of words on these two pages.
- ☆ Then count to **check**.

Book 1

estimate	check

Book 2

estimate	check

Book 3

estimate	check

Book 4

estimate	check

Now try this!

- **Find some books for older children.**
- **Estimate the number of words on page 8.**
- **Then count to check.**

Teachers' note Provide each pair of children with four reading books of an appropriate level. (Children who can count confidently could be given reading books with more words per page.) Stress that the more they practise estimating, the better they will become at it, and that they should not worry if their estimates are not very close. Encourage discussion and co-operation between the children in each pair and ensure that they both try to agree on each estimate.

Developing Numeracy
Using & Applying Maths
Year 1
© A & C BLACK

Garden centre: 1

Make decisions and record information

Use the price list on *Garden centre: 2*.

☆ Choose a packet of seeds and a tool.

☆ Work out the total cost.

☆ How many different totals can you find?

Now try this!

• **Work with a friend. Answer this question.**

I bought 3 things. I paid £16. What might they be?

• **Make up your own questions to ask.**

Teachers' note The children will need a copy of the price list on page 25. Let them record their choices of seeds and tools in their own way: for example, by drawing the choices or by writing the prices or words. For the extension activity, encourage the children to ask and answer their own questions: for example, 'What would be the most expensive bill if I bought two tools? What if I bought only seeds?'

**Developing Numeracy
Using & Applying Maths
Year 1
© A & C BLACK**

Garden centre: 2

Make decisions and record information

Price list

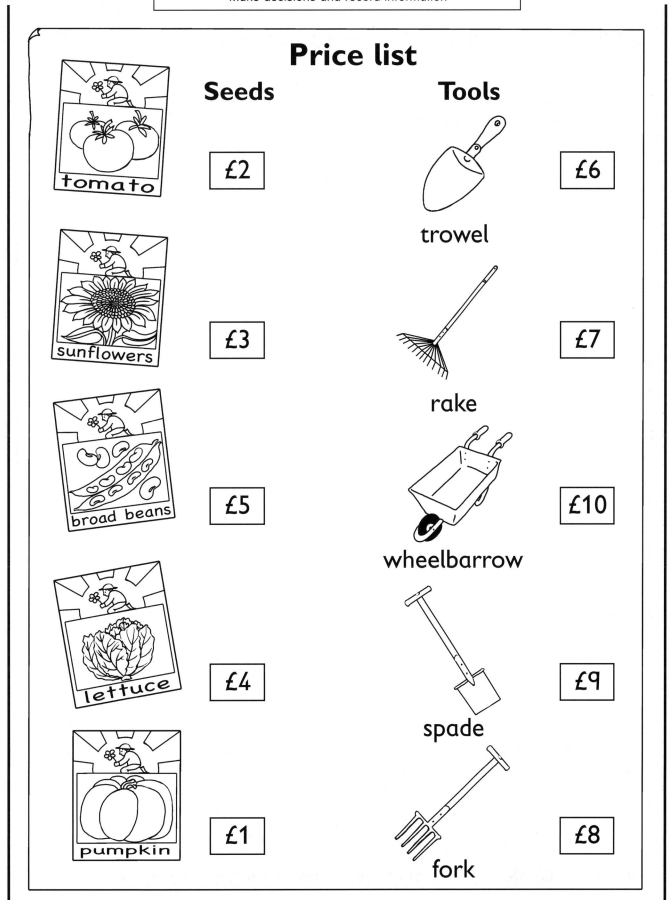

Seeds

tomato £2

sunflowers £3

broad beans £5

lettuce £4

pumpkin £1

Tools

trowel £6

rake £7

wheelbarrow £10

spade £9

fork £8

Teachers' note This sheet should be used in conjunction with page 24.

Developing Numeracy
Using & Applying Maths
Year 1
© A & C BLACK

Purses

Be systematic

Each purse holds $\boxed{5}$ coins. What could they be?

- **Choose from these coins.**

- **Write the total.**

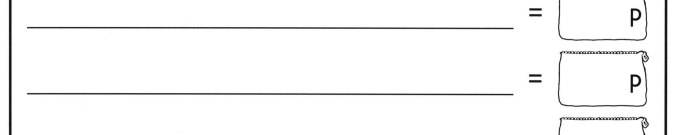

$1p + 1p + 1p + 1p + 1p$ = 5 P

= P

= P

= P

= P

= P

= P

= P

= P

- **Work with a friend.**

- **List all the different totals you have found.**

Can you find any others?

Teachers' note Remind the children that there are exactly five coins in each purse and that they could all be the same coin or they could be different. Encourage them to ask their own questions: for example, 'What is the most money that could be in the purse using only these coins? What is the least amount of money?' Make a class list of all the totals found and order them to encourage the children to look for others and to work systematically (see page 9).

**Developing Numeracy
Using & Applying Maths
Year 1
© A & C BLACK**

26

Hop frog

Look for patterns and be systematic

- **How many hops** from 11 to 5 ? __6__ hops

  from 10 to 2 ? ____ hops

  from 12 to 8 ? ____ hops

  from 9 to 3 ? ____ hops

- **Find 7 different ways of hopping back** 5 hops .

from ⬡ to ⬡   from ⬡ to ⬡

from ⬡ to ⬡   from ⬡ to ⬡

from ⬡ to ⬡   from ⬡ to ⬡

from ⬡ to ⬡

There are 7 ways of hopping back 5 hops .

- **How many different ways are there of**

  hopping back 2 hops , 6 hops **and** 8 hops ?

Teachers' note The first part of the activity encourages the children to think about the number of hops between two numbers. Ensure the children understand that they are counting the hops and not the numbers that lie between them.

Developing Numeracy
Using & Applying Maths
Year 1
© A & C BLACK

Teddy totals

Look for patterns and generalise

- ⬚Add⬚ **the numbers on the ears.**

- **Write the total on the teddy's tummy.**

- **Look at the teddies with the same totals.**

- **Talk to a friend about what you notice.**

- **Draw 2 teddies.**

- **Write numbers on their ears that make the same total.**

Teachers' note At the start of the lesson, discuss suitable strategies for finding the totals, in particular counting on from the larger number. Some children may benefit from using a number line. Encourage the children to look closely at the numbers in each pair of teddies, noticing the similarity between the digits and using this pattern for their own teddies (choosing one 'teens' number and one single-digit number for the first teddy, and then swapping the units/ones digits for the second teddy).

**Developing Numeracy
Using & Applying Maths
Year 1
© A & C BLACK**

Crazy cats

Generalise

Sam hits the ball under all 4 cats in any order. He scores the points on each cat.

He could go in this order: **4** then **3** then **1** then **2**

We can write this as: ___4 + 3 + 1 + 2___

What is his total score?

• **Find other orders. Write the totals.**

_____ ☐   _____ ☐

_____ ☐   _____ ☐

_____ ☐   _____ ☐

• **This cat is added to the game.**

• **Write different orders and find the totals.**

Teachers' note Explain to the children that each time, Sam must hit the ball under each of the cats once only. There are 24 different orders (see page 9 for solutions). If appropriate, the children could combine their different orders into a class list, organising them so that all starting with 1, then 2, then 3 and then 4 are put in groups to encourage systematic working.

Developing Numeracy
Using & Applying Maths
Year 1
© A & C BLACK

29

Daddy long legs

Be systematic and look for patterns

There are many ways of climbing 5 stairs.

1 stair at a time	2 stairs, then 3 stairs	5 stairs at once!

1 + 1 + 1 + 1 + 1	2 + 3	5

• Find other ways of climbing 5 stairs.

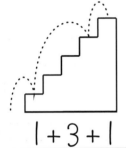

1 + 3 + 1
_____

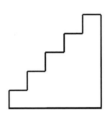
_____

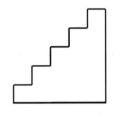
_____

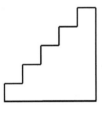
_____

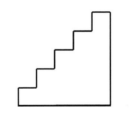
_____

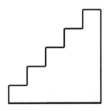
_____

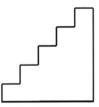
_____

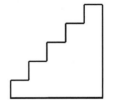
_____

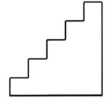
_____

• What if there were 6 stairs?

Teachers' note Remind the children that there are 5 stairs and so each addition they write should have a total of 5. Encourage them to ask their own questions: for example, 'What if we started with 3 steps at once? How many ways could we climb the last two?' For differentiation, the children could be asked to consider more or fewer stairs. Make a class list of all the ways found and order them to encourage the children to look for others and to work systematically (see page 9 for solutions).

**Developing Numeracy
Using & Applying Maths
Year 1
© A & C BLACK**

Look for patterns and generalise

| 1 | 2 | 3 | 4 | 5 | 6 | 7 | 8 | 9 | 10 | 11 | 12 |

3 and 4 are number neighbours.

• Add all the number neighbours.

$3 + 4 = 7$

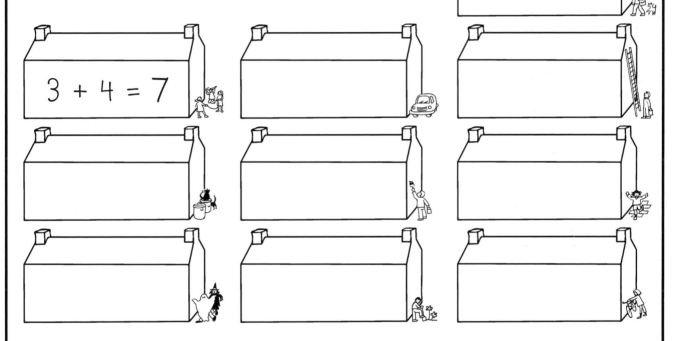

• Look at all your answers. Colour them below.

| 1 | 2 | 3 | 4 | 5 | 6 | 7 | 8 | 9 | 10 | 11 | 12 |
| 13 | 14 | 15 | 16 | 17 | 18 | 19 | 20 | 21 | 22 | 23 | 24 |

Now try this!

• Explain to a friend what you notice.
• Try adding other number neighbours.

Teachers' note Ensure the children understand what is meant by number neighbours (consecutive numbers). Encourage them to observe and describe what they notice about the totals of number neighbours and to test other pairs to check their ideas. The children could extend this activity to add three numbers in a row and examine the results.

**Developing Numeracy
Using & Applying Maths
Year 1
© A & C BLACK**

31

Flying kites

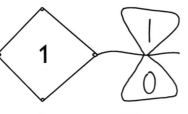

Each kite shows a `total`**.**

• Find pairs of numbers

which make the total.

Write them on the bows.

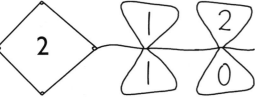

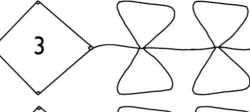

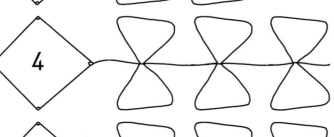

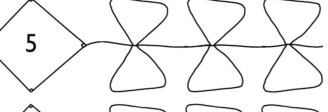

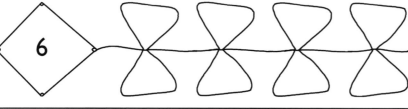

• Draw these kites. How many bows?

 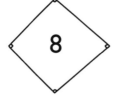 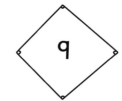

• What do you notice?

• Test your idea using other kite numbers.

Teachers' note If necessary, give the children 0–10 number cards to help them find new ways of making each total. Begin the lesson by discussing ways of making the total 6 (see page 10). For the extension activity, encourage the children to notice patterns in the number of bows on each kite and to use what they notice to predict the number of bows on kites showing different totals, such as 10 or 11. They can check their predictions by drawing the kites for these totals.

**Developing Numeracy
Using & Applying Maths
Year 1**
© A & C BLACK

Ten green bottles

- **Pick** 2 **numbers from the bottles.**
- **Find the** difference **between them.**
- **Try other numbers.**

Record your work here.

- **Talk to a friend about what you recorded.**

Now try this!

- **Which answer was**

largest? smallest?

Teachers' note The focus of this activity is to help children begin to realise the importance of recording things clearly so that others can understand their thinking. Rather than asking the children to use particular recording methods, allow them to use whatever approach they choose. Some may draw sets of objects and use informal symbols to indicate taking away; some might use tallies; others might use figures and the subtraction sign.

**Developing Numeracy
Using & Applying Maths
Year 1
© A & C BLACK**

Look for patterns and be systematic

Ella always gives herself [more] sweets than Ben.

- **Show all the ways that Ella can share out**

[8] sweets

8	0
7	

[10] sweets

I found [ ] ways

I found [ ] ways

- **How many ways do you <u>think</u> there are for Ella to share out [12] sweets?**

Now try this!

[ ] ways

*Ella **always** gets more!*

- **Make a list to find the answer.**

Teachers' note Ensure the children realise that Ben always has fewer sweets than Ella, and discuss what is meant by 'unfair'. Before beginning, suggest how many sweets two children might be given and ask the children to say whether it is fair or unfair. Encourage them to look for patterns in the number of different unfair ways they can find. Some children might benefit from having cubes or counters to rearrange when finding solutions.

**Developing Numeracy
Using & Applying Maths
Year 1
© A & C BLACK**

Roller-coaster rhyme

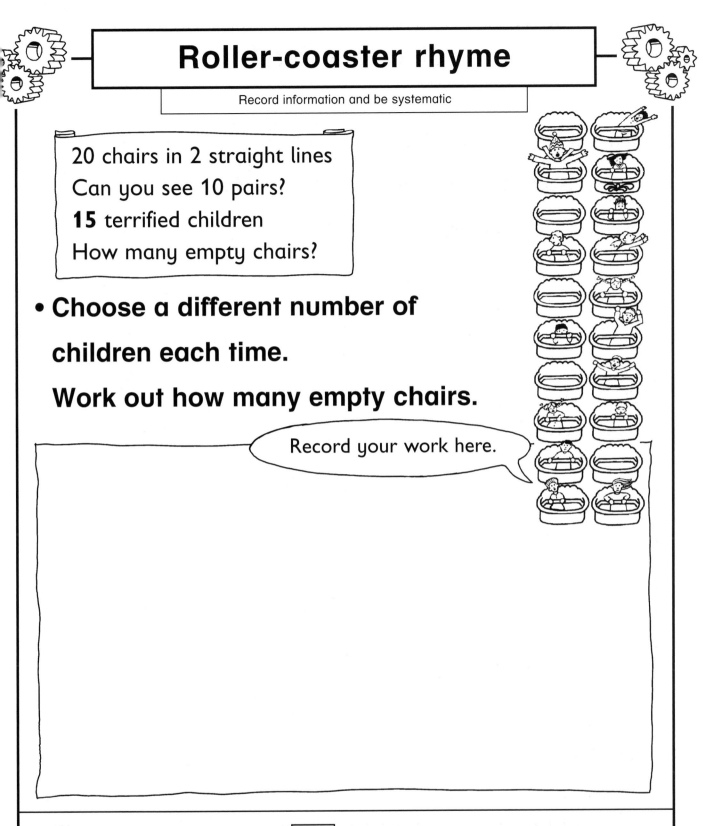

20 chairs in 2 straight lines
Can you see 10 pairs?
15 terrified children
How many empty chairs?

• **Choose a different number of**

children each time.

Work out how many empty chairs.

Record your work here.

• **If there were** 30 **chairs in 2 straight lines,**

how many pairs would there be?

• **If there were 15 children,**

how many empty chairs?

Now try this!

Teachers' note This activity could be introduced practically in the hall with 20 chairs set out in two lines. Say the rhyme several times, choosing a different number of 'terrified' children each time, and ask the class to work out how many empty chairs there are. Explain that you want them to find as many different solutions as they can, by choosing a different number of children in the rhyme each time. Encourage them to use any form of recording they choose (see page 10).

**Developing Numeracy
Using & Applying Maths
Year 1
© A & C BLACK**

Patchwork quilts

☆ The squares on the quilts are red, blue or yellow.

☆ Every quilt has at least 1 square of each colour.

☆ No touching squares are the same colour.

You need
a red, a blue and
a yellow pencil.

• **Colour the squares.**

Make each quilt different.

 • **Would you have any matching quilts if**

you turned any upside down?

Teachers' note Each child will need a red, a blue and a yellow pencil. (If these are not available, change the colour names on the sheet.) Ensure the children understand that all the squares should be coloured, that no touching squares horizontally or vertically should be the same colour and that each quilt should have at least one square of each colour. Encourage the children to compare their solutions with a partner and to observe any that are the same when rotated.

Developing Numeracy
Using & Applying Maths
Year 1
© A & C BLACK

Be systematic and visualise

- Put 8 counters on this grid.

- In the grids below,

  draw all the different

  ways you can arrange

  the counters.

  Here is one way.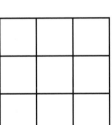

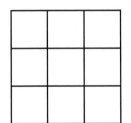 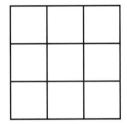 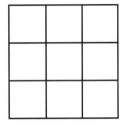 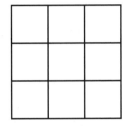

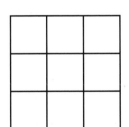 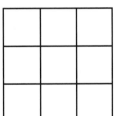 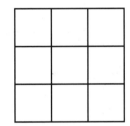

- How many different ways are there?

- How many squares in the grid?

- How could you arrange

  9 counters on this grid?

  Find all the different ways.

Teachers' note The children will need counters. For the extension activity, also provide a large 2 × 5 grid and squared paper. Allow the children to explore the tasks at their own pace. Rather than giving them clues, let them use trial and improvement approaches to discover for themselves that focusing on the empty space is much more useful than focusing on where the counters are.

Developing Numeracy
Using & Applying Maths
Year 1
© A & C BLACK

Pack the picnic

☆ Cut along the dotted lines below.

☆ Pack all the picnic things neatly in the basket.
Try different ways.

☆ Carefully glue them down when you have finished.

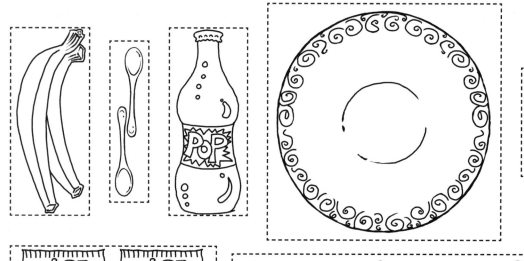

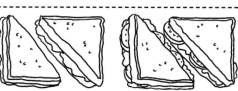

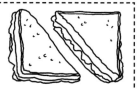

Teachers' note This sheet could be enlarged onto A3 and laminated, to make a more permanent resource. Explain that the picnic things must not overlap and make sure the children cut along the dotted lines, not around the pictures themselves. Once the children have glued the pieces into place, they can compare arrangements to see if there are different ways of fitting everything in. As an extension activity, the children could make their own picnic puzzle for a friend to solve.

**Developing Numeracy
Using & Applying Maths
Year 1
© A & C BLACK**

Look for patterns

The spider moves up and to

the right to catch a fly.

This route is called 1 2 2 1 .

The spider moves up 1 ,

right 2 , up 2 and right 1 .

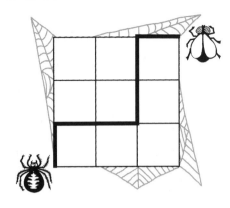

• **Write the names of these routes.**

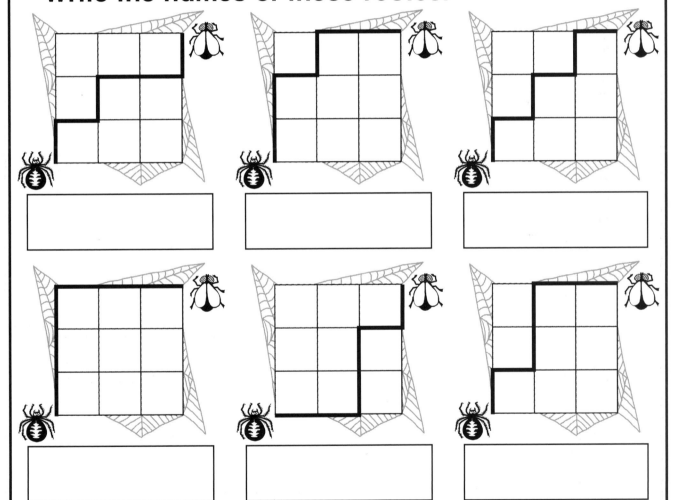

Teachers' note First draw a 3 × 3 grid on the board and demonstrate how a route can be drawn from the bottom left to the top right. Encourage the children to say how many squares up and to the right you have moved. Introduce and discuss the idea of calling a route by the number of squares moved in each direction: for example, 'up 3 and right 3' is called a '3 3' route. The activity on page 40 can be used to extend this work.

**Developing Numeracy
Using & Applying Maths
Year 1
© A & C BLACK**

Fly-catcher: 2

Look for patterns and be systematic

- ## Draw different routes from the spider to the fly.

- ## Name them.

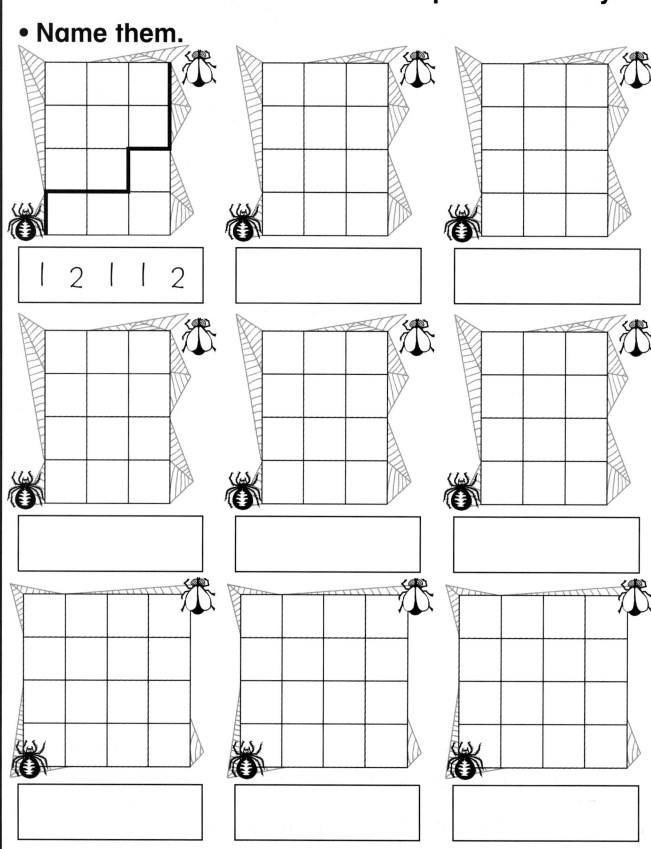

1 2 1 1 2

Teachers' note The children should first complete the activity on page 39. This activity introduces a 4 × 3 grid and a 4 × 4 grid. Remind the children that a route is called by the number of squares moved in each direction: for example, 'up 4 and right 3' is a '4 3' route. The children should be encouraged to find as many different routes as they can, to add the numbers in each route, and to show and explain their work to others.

**Developing Numeracy
Using & Applying Maths
Year 1
© A & C BLACK**

40

Toy stall

Be systematic and record information

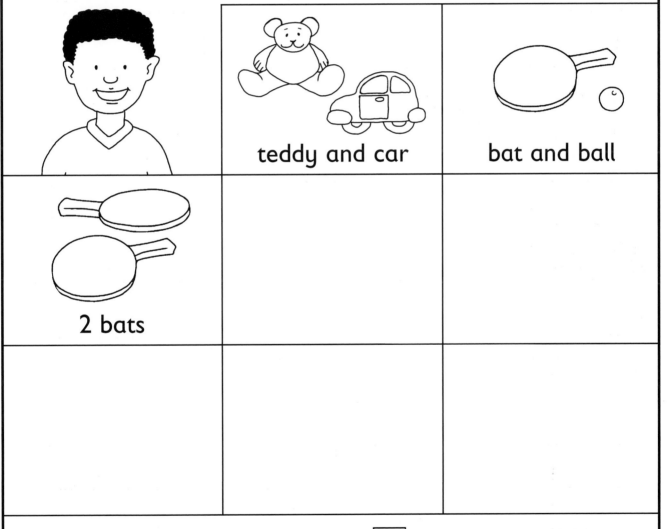

2 bats   1 teddy   1 car   2 balls

- **Jack buys** $\boxed{2}$ **toys. What could they be?**

Find 8 different answers.

	teddy and car	bat and ball
2 bats		

 - **What if Jack bought** $\boxed{3}$ **toys?**

Find 8 different answers.

Teachers' note Some children might find it useful to draw the six toys on separate pieces of paper so that they can move them around to find different solutions. Note that although there are two bats and two balls, 'bat and ball' only needs to be written once.

Developing Numeracy
Using & Applying Maths
Year 1
© A & C BLACK

Compare and reason

- **Cut out the letters along the dotted lines.**

- **What different ways can you sort them?**

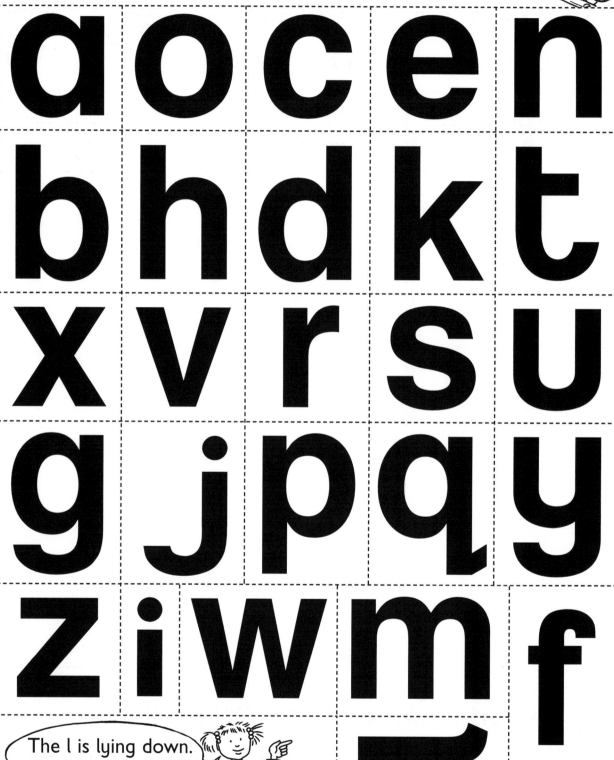

```
a o c e n
b h d k t
x v r s u
g j p q y
z i w m f
```

The l is lying down.
Stand it up.

Teachers' note Before discussing how the letters can be sorted, let the children explore and play with them in an unstructured way. Observe whether they are sorting according to size, in alphabetical order, or in more idiosyncratic ways. Then use the activity on page 43 to structure their sorting and to encourage them to record their ideas more formally.

Developing Numeracy
Using & Applying Maths
Year 1
© A & C BLACK

Letter sort: 2

Record information, compare and reason

You need the letters from *Letter sort: 1.*

• **Look at the chart below.**

• **Sort the letters. Write them in the correct place on the chart.**

straight lines only	straight and curved lines	curved lines only
	b	

• **Sort the letters in a different way.**

• **Draw a chart to show what you have done.**

Teachers' note The children will need the cards from page 42. In the extension activity, the children can sort the letters in any way they choose: for example, according to the number of lines that make up each letter or symmetrical properties. They can even explore which are vowels and which are consonants. Whichever way the letters are sorted, the focus should be on how best to show this in a chart, list or diagram. If appropriate, Venn and Carroll diagrams could be introduced.

Developing Numeracy
Using & Applying Maths
Year 1
© A & C BLACK

Shape shuffle

Visualise and compare

• **Cut out the cards. Join them to make new shapes. What shapes can you make?**

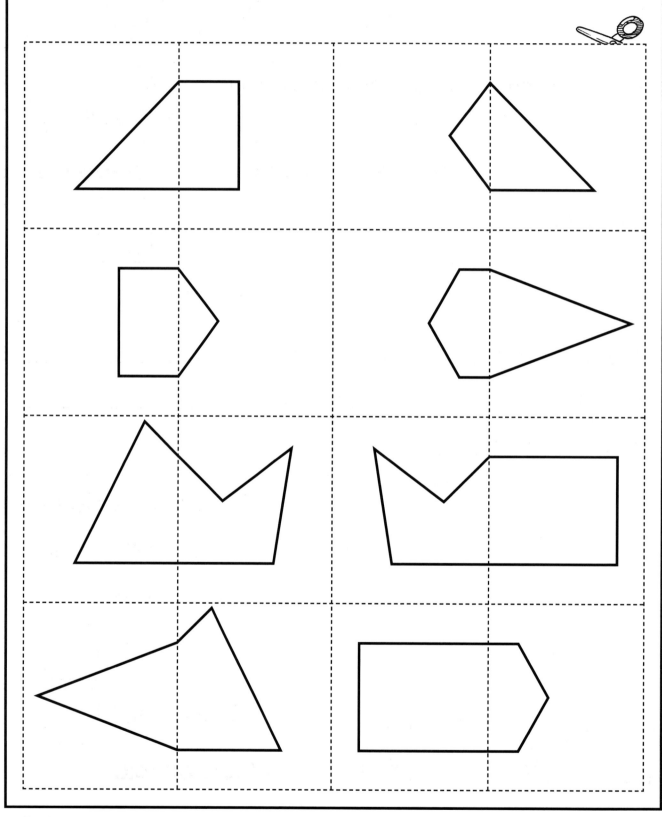

Teachers' note The children should be encouraged to experiment and play with the cards, joining pairs in different ways to make shapes. Ask the children to count the sides of each shape and, where possible, to name the shape. Observe whether the children choose to make symmetrical shapes by joining matching halves and encourage them to ask their own questions: for example, 'Is it possible to make a large triangle/rectangle?'

Developing Numeracy
Using & Applying Maths
Year 1
© A & C BLACK

Turn around

Look for patterns and reason

☆ **Always** start with the arrow at **A**.

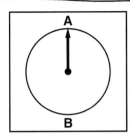

Cut out the pieces below to help you.

☆ If the arrow moves **1 half turn**, it points to **B**.

☆ If the arrow moves **2 half turns**, it points to **A** again.

• **Which letter does the arrow point to, if it moves**

4 half turns? ☐

3 half turns? ☐

5 half turns? ☐

6 half turns? ☐

• **How many half turns end on A?** _2_ ___ ___

• **How many half turns end on B?** _1_ ___ ___

• **Talk to a friend about what you notice.**

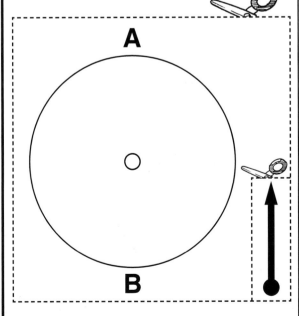

A

B

Now try this!

• **Which letter do you think the arrow will point to after**

9 half turns? ☐

10 half turns? ☐

• **Now check.**

Teachers' note The children should cut out the dial and arrow at the bottom of the page so that they can turn the arrow and check their answers. Remind them that the arrow should always point to A at the start. Encourage them to talk about any patterns they notice and to explain their thinking. Some children may benefit from having an enlarged copy of the dial and arrow, for more manageable turning. A split pin can then be used to fix the arrow to the centre of the dial.

Developing Numeracy
Using & Applying Maths
Year 1
© A & C BLACK

Mirror letters

Visualise, make predictions and test your ideas

This is half of a letter.

To see the whole letter, put

a mirror on the dotted line.

V
W

• **Tick** ✔ **which of these you <u>think</u> will**

make real letters. Then use a mirror to check.

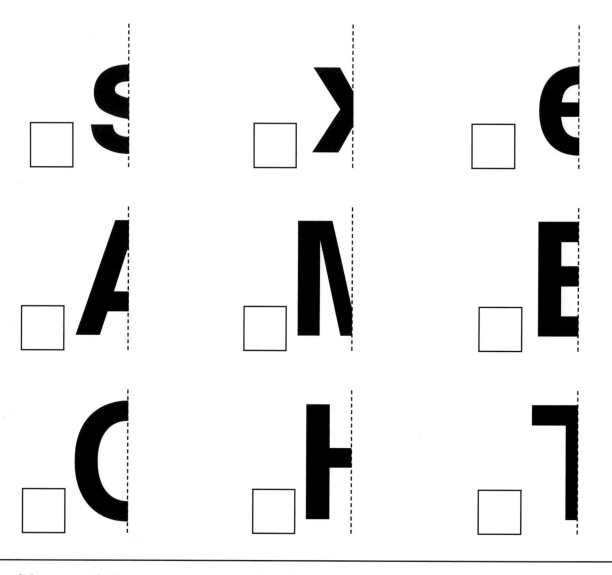

Now try this!

• **Draw your own half letter**

for a friend to try.

Teachers' note Provide mirrors once the children have predicted which will make real letters and discussed it with a partner. The children could also be asked to draw the reflections of the 'letter shapes' on the sheet. Some children may benefit from having a lower-case and upper-case alphabet to refer to. More confident children could explore which other letters of the alphabet can be reflected this way.

Developing Numeracy
Using & Applying Maths
Year 1
© A & C BLACK

Footprint fun

Make estimates and test your ideas

- Estimate how many cubes long the footprint is.
- Check by making a rod of cubes the same length as the footprint.

Footprint C

estimate ☐

check ☐

Footprint A

estimate ☐

check ☐

Footprint B

estimate ☐

check ☐

Now try this!

- How many cubes long is **your** shoe?

estimate ☐   check ☐

Teachers' note The children will require interlocking cubes to test their estimates. Ensure that they look carefully at the size of the interlocking cubes before making their estimates. Encourage them to estimate footprint A first and then check, before using this to help them make a better estimate for footprint B, and so on. For the extension activity, the children should visualise the length of their own shoe and then check their predictions with cubes.

**Developing Numeracy
Using & Applying Maths
Year 1
© A & C BLACK**

A toy train runs on a track.

- ## Cut out the cards. Arrange them to make 1 continuous track.

Now try this!

- ## How can you arrange the cards to make more than 1 track?

Teachers' note These cards could be enlarged onto card and laminated to use as a classroom game. Alternatively, give the children a sheet each for them to cut out their own cards. Ask them to try arranging the pieces so that one continuous track is created. They should compare solutions to see whether everyone made the same one or whether there is a variety of solutions (see page 12).

Developing Numeracy
Using & Applying Maths
Year 1
© A & C BLACK